This book belongs to:

_____

This book is dedicated to Reese and Emerson.
Thank you for inspiring me, believing in me
and for being my little cheerleaders. Forever beside me, cheering
me on.

ISBN: 979-8-9867933-3-7
Distribution: Anaheim, California

For information address www.tenillebwrites.com or email tenillejb@gmail.com

Book illustrated by Ira Baykovska - www.baykovska.com

A doctor, a lawyer, an artist, or a waiter,
A singer, a chef, or an Olympic ice skater.
There are so many jobs that I could select...

...but maybe, I'll be an architect.

As a stamp collector, I would hold
Thousands of stamps. Some new, some old.
I'd search the whole world for more stamps to collect...

…but maybe,
I'll be an architect.

As a politician, I would strive
To create new laws to help people thrive.
Maybe, I will be the next president you would elect…

…but maybe,
I'll be an architect.

As a vet, I would care for all the pets.
Nurse them back to health. I'd have no regrets.
Yes, I think I would be the very best vet...

As a surgeon, I'd save lives
Transplanting organs with surgical knives.

My hands would be so clean
and I would always disinfect...

...but maybe, I'll be an architect.

As a lawyer, I would always fight
For my clients with all my might.
In front of judges, I'd say 'I OBJECT'…

…but maybe,
I'll be an architect.

As a bodyguard, I would look real tough!
I'd tell fans of my client, "Alright. That's enough."
My business would be to defend and protect...

...but maybe, I'll be an architect.

As a detective, I would solve crimes!
I would search for evidence all the time.
I'd bring them downtown,
to check out the suspect...

As a Librarian, I'd compete
To keep my library quiet and neat.
I would tell them, you'd better show my
books some respect...

...but maybe, I'll be an architect.

As an explorer, I'd go far, to places thrilling and bizarre.
I'd tell my grandkids about all the places I have trekked...

...but maybe,
I'll be an
architect.

As a scientist, I'd brew potions,
And invent things to save the oceans.
Maybe I would even have frogs to dissect...

...but maybe, I'll be an architect.

...but maybe I'll be an architect.

As a director, there would be tons of movies I would make
Box office hits, make no mistake.
I'd fall in love with crazy special effects...

As a teacher, I would give away knowledge
To help all of my students get into college.
Piles of papers, oh man, I'd correct…

…but maybe,
I'll be an architect.

As an interior designer, I would create spaces
To make houses into homes. Make rooms perfect places.
The fanciest furnishings, I would select…

...but maybe, I'll be an architect.

In many careers, I would excel.
I'd work really hard. I'd do really well,
in all these careers, you could place a bet…

…but maybe, I'll be an architect.

CPSIA information can be obtained
at www.ICGtesting.com
Printed in the USA
LVHW071646021122
732174LV00001B/1

Maybe I'll be an ARCHITECT

I am so young, there's so many options to me.
There are so many careers, I'm not sure what I'll be.
But one job just keeps calling, one job feels correct...

...maybe I'll be an architect.

Maybe I'll be an Architect is not just a book about becoming an architect and exploring careers in design and construction. It is also about discovering the wonderful world of work. It teaches little ones about the diversity of possible careers available in our world, and if they put their minds to it, they can be anything they want to be. This exciting picture book is for parents who wish to encourage young readers to use their imagination while inspiring them to explore STEM (science, technology, engineering and mathematics) related careers.

ISBN 979-8-9867933-3-7

9 798986 793337

Cover art and cover design by Jade Le

Climb, Soar, Swim, Explore!

Kathryn Egly

Illustrator: Cedric Taylor